WALKING WITH JESUS

Six weeks of devotions for body and spirit

Susan Martins Miller

Healthy Living
for Church and Home
✚ RESOURCES FROM CHURCH HEALTH

Founded in 1987, Church Health is a charitably funded, faith-based, not-for-profit organization with a mission to *reclaim the church's biblical commitment to care for our bodies and our spirits.* Church Health provides comprehensive, high-quality, affordable health care to uninsured and underserved individuals and their families and gives people tools to live healthier lives. With the generous support of volunteer providers, the faith community, donors and community partners, we work tirelessly to improve health and well-being so that people can experience the full richness of life. For more information visit www.ChurchHealth.org.

Walking with Jesus: Six Weeks of Devotions for Body and Spirit
© 2013, 2020 Church Health Center, Inc. Memphis, TN

Scripture quotations contained herein are from the New Revised Standard Version Bible, copyright 1989, Division of Christian Education of the National Council of the Churches of Christ in the United States of America, and are used by permission. All rights reserved.

ISBN: 978-1-62144-066-6

Healthy Living for Church and Home brings you practical tools and insights to help you faithfully create habits to honor God and know fullness of life.

Walking with Jesus is part of the Ways to Wellness series, which also includes *Walking with Abraham and Sarah* and *Walking with Paul.*

Written by Susan Martins Miller.

Cover and interior design by Lizy Heard.

Our Mission

CHURCH HEALTH is a faith-based organization. Each day, we stand ready to care for people who are hurting but live within a health care system that has left them behind. Our neighbors come seeking help, yet what they find is much deeper and more healing. They discover hope for a better life.

The Bible calls us to follow Jesus, which means helping people farther along the path to knowing God by showing God's love through our actions to heal both body and spirit. Because the Bible guides our understanding of God's love as well as God's calling for us, we share the Bible's commitment to bring wellness and hope to people of all circumstances.

We know from history that Christians have always cared for the underserved, both in body and spirit. Jesus asks us to care about what he cares about—wellness and wholeness of all people. Healing that flows through personal care, preventive activities, medical methods, and health technology announce that God is present among us.

God invites us to participate in the overarching story of God's love in the world. The commitment to care for bodies and spirits belongs to the church—both locally and worldwide—because the church belongs to Jesus.

In Memphis, Tennessee, Church Health provides clinical services to uninsured and underserved individuals in the areas of medical, dental, optometry, physical rehabilitation, and behavioral health, along with wellness services in nutrition, life health coaching, child well-being, and disease prevention. Our funding comes from charitable sources, and hundreds of volunteers augment our staff to care for thousands of patients. Beyond Memphis, we reach across the country and around the globe with a ministry of faith community nurses and publications for healthy living.

Your purchase and use of this publication shares in our mission to care for bodies and spirits in a way that shows the love and hope of Jesus on the road to living in healthier ways that honor God's love for us.

For more information visit www.ChurchHealth.org.

Introduction

WELCOME TO *Walking with Jesus*, a six-week experience designed to help you make small changes and simple lifestyle improvements in your health and to grow in faith by accomplishing three simple goals:

1. Add 2,000 more steps a day to your activity level.
2. Add 3 servings of vegetables to your daily meals.
3. Add 3 glasses of water (a total of 24 ounces) each day to your daily fluids.

An inspiring devotional dimension reminds you of the connection between health in body and spirit. As you work on physical health goals, daily Scripture readings and meditations help you follow the routes that Jesus walked and nurture your spirit as well.

GETTING STARTED

You may choose to complete *Walking with Jesus* on your own, with a friend or two, or as part of a program organized through your congregation or community group.

To get started, you'll want to know the baseline for how many steps you take in a typical day, how many servings of vegetables you eat, and how much water you drink.

1. **STEPS.** If you don't have a good idea of the number of steps you take in a day, plan on using the first three days to maintain a normal activity level, but keep track of your steps. You can use a pedometer or convert minutes of activity into steps using the Activity Conversion Chart on page 11. Average your number of steps during the first three days to set your baseline.

   For instance, Tom walked, 5,050 steps on Monday, 4,123 steps on Tuesday, and 6,233 steps on Wednesday. This adds up to a total of 15,406 steps. He'll divide the number by three to get an average of 5,135 steps per day. This is Tom's baseline.

   Then the goal will be to increase the daily steps by 2,000. If your baseline is about 5,000 steps, then you'll aim for 7,000 steps each day. If your baseline is 3,000 steps, then you'll aim for 5,000. You won't be comparing yourself to anyone else—only where you've been and where you want to go.

2. **VEGETABLES.** For three days, record how many servings of vegetables you eat. One serving is one-half cup cooked or one cup raw vegetables. Find your

average for the three days. That is your baseline. The goal is to add three more. If your average is two servings, aim for five. If your average is four, aim for seven.

3. **WATER.** For three days, keep track of how many times you drink at least eight ounces of water. Find your average for the three days. That is your baseline. Adding three glasses per day (a total of 24 ounces) can be as simple as drinking eight ounces (one cup) of water at each of three meals.

— MY PERSONAL RECORD —

Program Start Date: ....

My baseline steps ....   My steps goal ....

My baseline vegetables ....   My vegetables goal ....

My baseline water ....   My water goal ....

BENEFITS OF *WALKING WITH JESUS*

The eating and physical activity patterns of the majority of Americans have made us the most overweight nation in the world. More than 60 percent of American adults do not get the recommended 30 minutes of physical activity in a day, and 25 percent are not physically active at all. Nearly two-thirds of adults are overweight, with the average person gaining one or two pounds each year.

This six-week experience will:
· Inspire individuals, groups of friends, or whole congregations to engage in fun, simple ways to become more active and eat more healthfully (and move toward a healthy weight as needed).
· Create a supportive network for changes in individual and congregational behavior.
· Encourage everyone who participates to use their gifts to live a healthy life.

It's all about energy balance! We can manage weight gain by creating a healthier balance between the amount of energy burned and the types and amount of food consumed throughout a normal day. Small changes, such as the three goals in this program, can make a difference without creating a sense of impossibility or failure. The key is reasonable and achievable goals. Big change doesn't happen all at once, but one step at a time—literally.

TOOLS IN THIS BOOK

You'll want to keep a Bible handy as you read each day's meditation. Many Bibles include maps that may help you identify locations mentioned in the passages you read. A simple **MAP**, such as on the back cover, gives you an appreciation for the places and distances Jesus traveled.

Each day's reading page also includes a **DAILY HEALTH JOURNAL** where you can record your number of steps for that day and check off whether you met the goals of adding 2,000 steps, 3 servings of vegetables, and 3 glasses of water. At the end of each week, transfer your checkmarks to a summary chart and see how you did for the week overall.

In addition to the daily meditations, each day provides a new **HEALTH TIP** to share health information or encourage you to incorporate what you already know into your daily routines.

At the close of this introductory material, you'll also find **TIPS FOR ADDING STEPS TO YOUR DAY** and an **ACTIVITY CONVERSION CHART** to help you calculate how other physical activity equates to added steps. Bicycling, gardening, yoga, rollerblading—it all counts toward walking. If you would also like to trim calories, a bonus goal, you'll find **TIPS FOR CUTTING 100 CALORIES**.

To begin your six weeks of walking, consider using the Self-assessment on page 13 that invites you to record you baseline habits and attitudes. Share this with a friend or turn it in to a project coordinator if you are part of a congregational program. At the end of six weeks, you'll have another opportunity to answer similar questions, evaluate your progress, and set new goals.

WALKING WITH JESUS IN A GROUP

Many features of *Walking with Jesus* are for individual use—keeping the Daily Health Journal, setting personal goals, and seeking spiritual inspiration in the daily reflections you can read at any time of the day. This doesn't mean you have to be on your own. You might be a leader looking for a simple program to use in your congregation to encourage healthy habits, or you might be someone who wants to gather a few friends for a shared path for six weeks of accountability as you all set reasonable goals and support each other in reaching them. Whether a handful of friends or a congregation-wide program, *Walking with Jesus* works well for group use.

Here are a few tips.

1. **ORDER COPIES IN ADVANCE.** If you're reading this copy of *Walking with Jesus* and want to organize a group, make it easy by ordering copies for your group at one time. Make sure everyone has a copy before the start of the six-week period.

2. **HOLD A BRIEF LAUNCH MEETING.** This doesn't have to be long or involved. The purpose is to draw attention to the tools in the book and agree together how you want to use them in your group. This gets everyone on the same page so that as you support each other over the six-week period, everyone speaks the same language. Will you share the pre- and post-assessments? What do you think will be the best ways you'll want to add steps or cut calories from the tips lists provided? How often will you connect with each other?

3. **PLAN WAYS TO TOUCH BASE.** Knowing how to support each other will be important. Some ideas are:

- Meet for a few minutes during the coffee time or adult Sunday school hour on Sunday mornings and talk about successes and challenges of the week. Share which reflections encouraged you the most. Pray for one another.
- Set up a closed Facebook group and post daily questions for members to respond to about how they're doing on their health journeys. Consider ways to tie questions to the daily reflections or health tips.
- Use a group e-mail, text message, or Messenger process for frequent private contact with words of encouragement, tips, and brief prayers.
- Plan times when members of the group can physically walk together and share their successes and challenges and get some steps in at the same time. The whole group doesn't have to walk together. This could be a time for two to four people to meet up according to schedules or locations.

4. **SHARE A CLOSING MEAL.** At the end of six weeks, share a healthy meal. Invite participants who shared the walking journey to bring healthy dishes that reflect ways they changed their eating during the six weeks. There might be some recipe swapping!

Each new healthy habit becomes a foundation for the next one. One of the best ways to celebrate progress is to know your starting point and be able to look back after six weeks and see changes. No change for the better is too small to celebrate.

TIPS FOR ADDING STEPS TO YOUR DAY

Making simple choices to add steps throughout your day will result in an added 2,000 steps before you know it. Try some of these ideas.

Choose the stairs instead of the elevator.
Park in the back row of the parking lot.
Mow the lawn with a walking mower.
Walk with a friend during your lunch break.
Pace around the house while talking on the phone.
Instead of e-mailing or calling a coworker, walk down the hall and have a face-to-face interaction.
Make several trips and up and down the stairs when doing laundry and household chores.
Pass the drive-thru and walk into the restaurant or bank.
Tour a museum, zoo, or nature preserve.
Volunteer to walk dogs for an animal shelter.
Walk to yard sales to shop for bargains.
Circle around the block once before bringing in the mail.
Walk on short errands, such as a nearby store, post office, or dry cleaners.
Go window shopping at the mall.
Meet a friend for lunch at a restaurant you can walk to.
Play a round of golf but pass on the golf cart.

TIPS FOR CUTTING 100 CALORIES

Small changes in food preparation and portion size can quickly add up and have a dramatic impact on your health. Each one of these options will allow you to trim 100 calories out of your daily intake and meet your daily goal.

Select skim, one percent or two percent milk instead of whole milk.
Use a small glass for juice and a small bowl for cereal.
Use cooking spray in place of butter or margarine.
Put lettuce, tomato, onions, and pickles on your burger or sandwich instead of cheese.
Prepare tuna or chicken salad with fat-free or light mayonnaise.
Select soft corn tortillas instead of hard shell tortillas.
Replace a can of soda with mineral water.
Enjoy your salad without the croutons.
Leave three or four bites on your plate.
Use a fat-free, light, or reduced-fat cheese, sour cream, or salad dressing in place of regular.
Limit meat portions to three or four ounces—the size of a deck of cards.
Steam vegetables rather than frying with butter.
Add 1/4 less cheese to spaghetti and lasagna. Customize the dish with fresh seasonal vegetables.
Bake, broil, or grill chicken instead of frying.
Share one serving of dessert with a friend.
Substitute applesauce for vegetable oil when baking.
Choose 100 percent juice over juice cocktails and fruit punch.
Skip super-sized portions.
Choose a side salad or steamed vegetables instead of fries, pasta, or onion rings.
Dip your fork in salad dressing instead of pouring dressing over the salad.
Cut out one tablespoon of butter or oil from a recipe.
Use two egg whites in place of one whole egg.

ACTIVITY CONVERSION CHART

If you engage in physical activities other than walking, you can convert minutes of activity to steps for credit toward adding 2,000 steps per day to your usual routine.

Activity	Steps per Minute
Aerobics (low-impact)	125
Aerobics (moderate)	153
Aerobics (water)	100
Basketball	100
Bicycling (leisurely)	100
Bicycling (moderate)	200
Bicycling (stationary)	181
Cross country skiing	114
Dancing (all types)	133
Elliptical machine	203
Football	133
Gardening	73
Golf (walking)	100
Jogging (12 minutes per mile)	232
Hopping	51
Painting	78
Pilates	92
Racquetball	138
Resistance training	74
Rollerblading	200
Rowing (leisurely)	74
Rowing (moderate)	153
Running (10 minutes per mile)	290
Running (7.5 minutes per mile)	391
Scrubbing floors	92
Soccer	144
Stair climbing (down)	72

Continued on page 12.

Continued from page 11.

Activity	Steps per Minute
Stair climbing (up)	205
Stretching	6
Swimming	200
Tai chi	8
Tennis	200
Volleyball	90
Walking	125
Washing car	72
Waterskiing	136
Weight lifting	100
Yoga	50

— Self-assessment —

If you are using Walking with Jesus *as part of a group or congregation, answer these questions before you begin and consider sharing your answers with the project coordinator or friends in your group.*

Name: ....

Congregation or Community Organization: ....
....

1. How many days a week do you engage in some type of mild to moderate physical activity (walking slowly, gardening, housework, window shopping, and so on)?   Days per week ....

2. How many days a week do you engage in some type of moderate to vigorous physical activity (brisk walking, running, riding a bike, dancing, playing a sport and so on)?   Days per week ....

3. Which answer best describes how you feel about the following?

	I have no plans to	I plan to in the future	I plan to immediately	I have been doing so for *fewer* than six months	I have been doing so for *more* than six months
Increasing physical activity					
Improving nutrition					

4. To what degree do you feel that your physical health and spiritual health are connected?

○ Not at all   ○ Quite a bit
○ A little bit   ○ Extremely
○ Moderately

CUT HERE

Begin Your Journey
HERE

Prepare the Way

MARK 1:2-3

"Prepare the way of the Lord, make his paths straight."
—Mark 1:3

T HE GOSPEL OF MARK opens with a summons to hope. God is coming! Get ready! The wilderness days will end! In the opening verses, the writer quotes two Old Testament prophets, Malachi and Isaiah, telling listeners that God is about to break into their lives in a new way.

In the ancient Near East, important figures such as officials or kings sent messengers ahead to make sure the way would be clear for arrival, the road would be ready for travel, and the local residents would be prepared to welcome the guests.

We know God wants to come to us. Less often, perhaps, we ask ourselves if we are prepared to welcome God's arrival. Life can feel like a wilderness—too big, not enough resources, isolated, far away from where we want to be. Yet even there the good news reaches us that God is coming, and we hear the urging to "prepare the way of the Lord."

Will we see and hear when God comes, even if we are in a wilderness season?

Certainly God will come to us as we walk with Jesus through the Gospel of Mark and open our hearts to the images of health and wholeness that abound. Certainly God will come to us as we learn to make small changes that will lead us toward abundant living.

HEALTH

Are you ready to start making a few small changes? It's important to set goals that are challenging and attainable. Don't feel like you are doing it alone, though. Share your goals with people who can support you. Enjoy the satisfaction of not only reaching your goals but also bringing others along.

— DAILY HEALTH JOURNAL —

Number of steps.................................

O Add 2,000 steps

O Add 3 servings of vegetables

O Add 3 glasses of water

Into the Jordan

MARK 1:9-11

And a voice came from heaven, "You are my Son,
the Beloved; with you I am well pleased."
—Mark 1:11

THE JORDAN RIVER IS THE longest and most important river in Palestine. Flowing from the north, it curves and winds its way south into the Sea of Galilee and farther, dropping in elevation, until it reaches the Dead Sea. The ancient Israelites entered Canaan, the promised land, by crossing the Jordan, and John the Baptist's ministry was along the Jordan River. This is where John met Jesus, when Jesus arrived and asked John to baptize him.

Jesus' baptism in the Jordan was the first significant public event in his life and the beginning of his own ministry announcing that the kingdom of God had come. As Jesus came up out of the water, the Holy Spirit descended like a dove and a voice spoke from heaven. God does not speak of pride in what Jesus has accomplished or stern instructions for how Jesus is supposed to carry out his work on earth. Rather, God speaks words of love. In that important moment in Jesus' life, a parent speaks to a son: "You are my Son, the Beloved."

We, too, are beloved by God. Jesus came into the world because of God's love for us. In times of striving, whether for greater accomplishments or better health, the greatest benefit may come by letting go of our own frail efforts and resting in the security that we are God's beloved.

HEALTH TIP

Water is life-sustaining; whether it is the water of baptism that signals the changing of lives or drinking water that refreshes and hydrates. How much water do you need every day? Take your body weight in pounds and divide by two. Drink that many ounces every day. People living in dry climates need an extra 16 ounces. Active people need extra water. Carry a water bottle while you walk on hot days, at work, or when traveling.

— DAILY HEALTH JOURNAL —

Number of steps.............................   ○ Add 3 servings of vegetables
○ Add 2,000 steps   ○ Add 3 glasses of water

The Wilderness Journey
MARK 1:12-13

... he was with the wild beasts; and the angels waited on him.
—Mark 1:13

FROM THE HIGH MOMENT of his baptism, Jesus went swiftly into the desert wilderness, where he was isolated for 40 days. Two other Gospel writers, Matthew and Luke, give more detail about what happened during these weeks of being tempted by Satan. In facing temptation, Jesus identified with the temptations we face, whether for greater power, greater pride, or greater riches—or for the rich taste of food and drink that feel good in the moment and cause regret later as most temptations do.

The unique element Mark includes is that Jesus was with wild beasts while he was tempted. During Jesus' lifetime, it's likely there was more danger from wild animals in that region than there might be now. The word of assurance for us is that the angels attended Jesus during a difficult time. Even Jesus needed God's care, and God provided it. Even in the wilderness Jesus was not separated from God.

And we are not separated from God in our wildernesses. None of us can claim we have faultlessly withstood temptation the way Jesus did, but we can claim the assurance of God's presence and care. God knows our weaknesses and needs even better than we do and graciously provides care and assurance to lead us out of testing times and toward health and wholeness

HEALTH TIP
Sun exposure is the main source of vitamin D. Even as little as five minutes per day brings benefit. At the other end of the spectrum, prolonged sun exposure can be a concern. Heat exhaustion or heat stroke can result from extreme exposure to the sun, and extended over-exposures brings risk of skin cancer. Use sunscreen any time you expect to be out in the sun for more than a few minutes.

— DAILY HEALTH JOURNAL —

Number of steps ....

O Add 2,000 steps

O Add 3 servings of vegetables

O Add 3 glasses of water

To Galilee

MARK 1:14-15

"The time is fulfilled, and the kingdom of God has come near."
—Mark 1:15

THE GOSPELS GIVE US the words of Jesus while teaching his disciples or preaching to the masses, but these key words from the beginning of the Gospel of Mark get right to the point. Jesus' message boils down to, "The time is fulfilled, and the kingdom of God has come near."

In Jesus, God's kingdom broke into human history, and Jesus invited us to live in that kingdom. Because Jesus said the kingdom has come near, we don't have to wait for a "someday" kingdom in heaven. While we still look forward to the final culmination of God's redemption of the world, we can experience right now the love and presence of God in our lives. We can experience right now the power of love toward one another, the strength that comes from compassion, the healing that breaks forth from generosity and forgiveness we receive from God and offer to one another.

The kingdom of God is not something only for later. It's for right now. Jesus said, "Repent and believe in the good news." That means to change direction and look toward God. We can choose to do this each moment of our health journeys. Will we make mistakes? Yes. Will we make choices we regret? Yes. But the good news of God's kingdom is the good news of fresh beginnings. Take a few minutes to think about your day and open yourself to the moments when you can intentionally make healthy choices.

HEALTH TIP

Being in the present moment reduces stress. Sometimes we fret so much about what might or might not happen later in the day or later in life that we miss what is beautiful or significant in *this* moment. Mindfulness is moment-by-moment awareness of our thoughts, feelings, and sensations. It can lower blood pressure, improve focus, make us more compassionate, and help us sleep better. When these things happen, we're better at relationships, work, and faith practices—all of which benefit health.

— **DAILY HEALTH JOURNAL** —

Number of steps...........................   ○ Add 3 servings of vegetables
○ Add 2,000 steps   ○ Add 3 glasses of water

Along the Sea of Galilee
MARK 1:16-20

"Follow me and I will make you fish for people."
—Mark 1:17

TWO FISHERMEN BROTHERS, Andrew and Simon (whom we also know as Peter) were at work on the Sea of Galilee on an ordinary day that turned extraordinary when Jesus said, "Follow me and I will make you fish for people." We can imagine that the summons did not fully make sense. Though they may well have encountered Jesus before this, could they be sure of who he was? And what did Jesus mean by fishing for people anyway? Even if Jesus was someone as great as the promised Messiah, following him would mean drastic changes to their lives. Were they ready? The answer is yes. Mark says they left their fishing nets "at once."

Jesus moved on to another pair of brothers, James and John, who also were fishermen. They were working with their father, Zebedee. What did he think? Did he urge them to go or beg them to stay? Mark says they followed Jesus.

Both sets of brothers made considerable changes. A routine life of fishing would become a life of frequent travel and days away from work and family. Jesus called, and the fishermen answered.

Are we also listening when Jesus calls, even if it means making changes? All the other disciples who followed Jesus stepped into a changed—and abundant— life. Though change in our pursuit of health can be scary or challenging, it can lead to a new level of living closer to God and others.

HEALTH TIP

In Palestine fish was the main source of nutrition, caught from the Sea of Galilee and enjoyed in abundance. Add more fish to your diet for heart health. Fish is a good source of protein and is lower in fat than beef, pork, or poultry. It's also loaded with minerals such as iron, zinc, and calcium.

— DAILY HEALTH JOURNAL —

Number of steps...........................

○ Add 2,000 steps

○ Add 3 servings of vegetables

○ Add 3 glasses of water

Six weeks of devotions for body and spirit **21**

DAY 6

To the Synagogue in Capernaum
MARK 1:21-28

"He commands even unclean spirits,
and they obey him."
—Mark 1:27

J ESUS TOOK HIS NEW disciples to Capernaum, a city along the Sea of Galilee where they had been fishing. Together they attended the synagogue and, following a custom of synagogue leaders inviting visitors to participate, Jesus taught the worshipers.

In the congregation that day was a man possessed by an "unclean" or evil spirit. The spirit recognized Jesus' authority—and the threat that Jesus was to an evil spirit. Jesus cast the spirit out of the man and restored him to health.

We might not think that a person with an unclean spirit would have been welcome in a traditional first-century Jewish house of worship, yet the man was there. Jesus did not ignore him or treat him as "less than" because of the spirit. By casting out the demon, Jesus welcomed the man into wholeness.

In ancient times, demon possession was considered a different category of illness than something such as paralysis or fever. Yet Jesus did not treat it any differently, and we learn from his example not to treat some illnesses as "real" and others as "not real" or some as "physical" and others as "spiritual." We do well to extend to ourselves the same grace. As you pursue better health, keep in mind that blaming yourself for failures does not restore well-being. Receive healing and stay on the path.

HEALTH TIP

People who are troubled often go to places of worship to seek solace or forgiveness. Research suggests that people who participate in religious communities and attend church regularly have better mental health, greater social support, and less anxiety over their problems. Congregations interested in expanding health ministry can begin by asking whether they are safe and healing communities for people who may come in troubled states.

--- **DAILY HEALTH JOURNAL** ---

Number of steps................................   ◯ Add 3 servings of vegetables
◯ Add 2,000 steps   ◯ Add 3 glasses of water

To Peter's House

MARK 1:29–34

He cured many who were sick with
various diseases, and cast out many demons.
—Mark 1:34

AFTER JESUS HEALED THE man with an unclean spirit (Mark 1:21–28), news spread quickly around Galilee. Jesus and his disciples left the synagogue and went to the home of Simon Peter and Andrew, perhaps for a meal. Simon's mother-in-law was in bed with a fever, and Jesus healed her. The illness left her so swiftly that she was able to get up and serve her guests.

Imagine settling in for a quiet meal and the doorbell rings incessantly. Perhaps people who had been with Jesus earlier in the day in the synagogue had watched to see where he would go next. Now they began to bring family and friends who were sick to Jesus to be healed. With the Sabbath over, they were free to carry things—including people who could not reach Jesus on their own. Mark says the "whole city" gathered. Unusual news draws a crowd. No doubt a crowd amassed to see what Jesus would do for all the sick.

He healed them. The simplicity of Jesus' response reminds us that God asks the same of us—to act with compassion, to see needs and meet them, to walk with each other toward greater wellness in body and spirit.

How do we bring people to Jesus for healing now? Who do you know who is in need of the healing that comes from knowing God is near? How can you help guide someone you care for?

HEALTH TIP

Setbacks are a part of progress. Characters undergo radical transformation during a 30-minute TV program, but life is not that way. As you do your part in seeking healing in your life, both in body and spirit, don't set yourself up for failure by expecting to avoid all setbacks. Avoid making excuses that will talk you out of even trying, but at the same time allow grace, not guilt, to keep you moving forward.

— DAILY HEALTH JOURNAL —

Number of steps.................................   O Add 3 servings of vegetables
O Add 2,000 steps   O Add 3 glasses of water

Week One in Review

THIS WEEK YOU ESTABLISHED baseline steps for the *Walking with Jesus* program. Were you surprised to see how many steps you were averaging in the first three days? Did you set aside more time to get the extra 2,000 steps? Taking time to be physically active is a journey, like many other challenges in our lives. The work may seem easier to do on some days than others, and we need to be intentional about remaining focused.

As Jesus invited others to journey with him, you can too. Partner with a friend, coworker, or fellow congregation members. Walking and other types of activity can be great ways to get to know someone or deepen a friendship. When no one is available to exercise with you, consider using the time to meditate as you exercise. Exercise can be a spiritual time as well as physical.

Take time now to tally your weekly steps and review your health goals. Transfer your daily steps in the space below. If you set a goal for all three categories, put checkmarks in the boxes where you reached your goal for each day.

*Transfer your daily steps in the space below. If you set a goal
for all three categories, put checkmarks in the boxes
where you reached your goal for each day.*

Number of steps	Add 2,000 steps	Add 3 vegetables	Add 3 glasses of water
Day 1	○	○	○
Day 2	○	○	○
Day 3	○	○	○
Day 4	○	○	○
Day 5	○	○	○
Day 6	○	○	○
Day 7	○	○	○

With the Crowds in Capernaum
MARK 2:1–12

"I say to you, stand up, take up your mat and go to your home."
—Mark 2:11

A FEW DAYS AFTER JESUS healed Peter's mother-in-law, the crowds were still coming. Mark gives us a picture of Jesus operating out of a house yet preaching to large groups. The story of four friends bringing a paralyzed man to Jesus is one of the most familiar Gospel stories. When they could not get in through the door, the friends cut through the clay-and-branches roof and lowered their friend to Jesus.

Jesus commended the faith of these friends, and he not only healed the paralyzed man's body but announced publicly that he forgave the man's sins as well. When the man picked up the mat he'd been lying on and walked out of the house in full view of the crowd, it was clear that preaching tells the good news of the kingdom of God, but so does healing.

God did not create us to live in isolation but to be connected to one another. When one person needs healing, others can help to bring it about. A web of personal connections contributes to overall health. We all need social support from our family and friends. A support system helps us to stick to exercise plans and other healthy lifestyle habits.

To what extent will we go to bring friends to Jesus—sharing the journey to health?

As you go through your day, reach out to others in small ways that will give big support to their efforts to make positive choices.

HEALTH TIP

Modern athletic shoes offer more support and comfort than the leather-strap sandals of Jesus' time and are a good investment for walking toward better health. Choose a shoe that fits comfortably and supports well. Allow for a finger width of space between your longest toe and the end of the shoe. Make sure the shoe is not so wide that your foot slides around inside. Socks that include synthetic material will reduce chafing and blistering.

— DAILY HEALTH JOURNAL —

Number of steps............................

O Add 2,000 steps

O Add 3 servings of vegetables

O Add 3 glasses of water

DAY 9

Dinner with Tax Collectors

MARK 2:13-17

"I have come to call not the righteous but sinners."
—Mark 2:17

THE FIRST DISCIPLES JESUS called were fishermen. In today's passage, he called Levi, also known as Matthew, who was a tax collector. This opened the door to a repeating picture of Jesus in Mark's Gospel as someone who was not afraid to befriend the friendless.

Jewish tax collectors worked for the occupying Roman government and were thus associated with the oppressors. This put them in a category with the worst of sinners. They were not even welcome in Jewish worship life. Yet Jesus showed no hesitation to have dinner with a houseful of tax collectors and other outcasts from society.

"Why does he eat with them?" the religious leaders asked. Eating with someone was a sign of friendship—as it often is now. How often do we think twice about whether we would want to share a meal with a particular person? How willing are we to enter the lives of other people?

Jesus answered, "I have come to call not the righteous but sinners." When we slip into self-righteousness, we risk denying our own need for the healing Jesus brings. We miss out on the possibility that we may bring wholeness to each other by recognizing that we all need healing. Jesus gives us the example of accepting hospitality and using the experience to connect with others in healing ways.

HEALTH TIP

Who you eat with can be an important aspect of making positive food choices. Being in the company of relaxed, welcoming diners can help anyone look forward to a healthy mealtime. Scripture is full of references to feasts and banquets, a way the early Palestinians demonstrated the virtue of hospitality. Use meal times to provide not only food but also the social support that undergirds well-being. Think of someone you'd like to share a meal with and pick up the phone.

— DAILY HEALTH JOURNAL —

Number of steps.............................   ○ Add 3 servings of vegetables
○ Add 2,000 steps   ○ Add 3 glasses of water

The Multitude in Galilee
MARK 3:7–10

*He told his disciples to have a boat ready for him
because of the crowd, so that they would not crush him.*
—Mark 3:9

JESUS TOOK CARE OF A LOT of people! His growing group of disciples traveled with him, and a "great multitude" followed him. This was not only the local people in Galilee, who might have witnessed a healing miracle, but also people from all of Israel and neighboring regions. News about what Jesus was doing had spread. "Great numbers" of people came from these other areas.

"Great multitude" and "great numbers"—Mark certainly wanted to impress on his readers the swelling popularity of Jesus. All who were sick wanted a chance to touch Jesus and be healed by this contact. Jesus' healing ministry was drawing crowds so large and insistent that Jesus made sure he was taking care of himself as well. He asked his disciples to have a boat ready, because it might be the best way to withdraw from the pressing crowds.

Some professions are full-time caregiving roles. Parents give care to their children. Neighbors look out for each other, especially in times of need. Aging parents require increasing levels of care from their children or others. In all of these ways, we help each other find health and wholeness. At the same time, we need to care for ourselves. Jesus' example in this short story in Mark 3 reminds us to follow his example not only in extending compassionate care to others but also in being mindful of keeping ourselves healthy enough to offer that care.

HEALTH TIP
We often have emotional ups and downs over the course of the day. Today, pay special attention to when you feel those highs and lows. How do you feel in the morning? After lunch? In the evening? Keep a record of your highs and lows, what events during the day might be contributing, and how you respond in terms of food and movement choices.

— DAILY HEALTH JOURNAL —

Number of steps................................
O Add 2,000 steps

O Add 3 servings of vegetables
O Add 3 glasses of water

The Family of Jesus

MARK 3:31–35

*"Whoever does the will of God is
my brother and sister and mother."*
—Mark 3:35

WE OFTEN FORGET THAT JESUS had a family. We remember Mary and Joseph from his birth or when he was left behind in Jerusalem at age 12, but it's easy not to think beyond those stories. Mark tells us that Jesus' mother and brothers came to see him. As Mark 3 comes to a close, Jesus has appointed the 12 disciples and continues to be pressed in on by the crowds. He was in a house that was so full that Jesus and the disciples did not even have the opportunity to eat (Mark 3:20). His family has become concerned. Jesus was exposing himself to risk because the religious leaders opposed him, and even with this danger Jesus persisted in teaching (3:22–30). His mother and brothers arrived to take him safely home. Perhaps they wanted to be sure Jesus understood what could happen if he kept on with his ministry. But they couldn't even get in the house, so they sent a message to him that they were there.

Jesus was teaching at the time—in between trying to grab bites of food—and he deftly turned the arrival of his family, with all their doubts, into a teachable moment for the crowd. They, too, could become part of Jesus' family by doing the will of God. We can show our connection to Jesus through our actions toward one another.

HEALTH TIP

Gratitude can help many stressful situations. What are you grateful for? At the end of each day, reflect on your day and make a list. Include even the small things—the birds who came to your feeder or the way your dog greets you. What people belong on a gratitude list? Which experiences? Give thanks before you go to bed, and check the list again in the morning to get the new day off to a healthy start.

— DAILY HEALTH JOURNAL —

Number of steps.............
⭕ Add 2,000 steps

⭕ Add 3 servings of vegetables
⭕ Add 3 glasses of water

Teaching Beside the Sea
MARK 4:30-32

*"With what can we compare the kingdom
of God, or what parable will we use for it?"*
—Mark 4:30

JESUS WAS ONCE AGAIN teaching by the sea. For the first time in the book of Mark, we see Jesus using parables to teach about the kingdom of God he came to announce. Whether speaking to crowds or going deeper in meaning with his closest followers, Jesus told stories and used images from ordinary life to illustrate truths about God's kingdom and the life of discipleship. Gospel writers Matthew, Mark, and Luke all record some of the parables of Jesus.

In Mark 4, the writer emphasizes the importance of soil conditions for seeds of the kingdom to grow, the mysterious potential for an unremarkable seed to sprout with life, and the reality that even something as small and insignificant as a mustard seed can grow into the greatness of the kingdom of God.

Jesus' first message in Mark 1:15 was that the kingdom of God has come near. The parable pictures underscore that the kingdom is all around us.

The kingdom is even in us. Let it become the biggest thing. We may yearn for a sign from heaven about a big decision or dream of doing something great for God with our lives. The answers may have such small beginnings that at first we do not recognize that even in our ordinary lives we participate in the kingdom of God and show its greatness to others. The most important thing is to be confident that God is at work in our lives and in our world.

HEALTH TIP
Exercise is important for overall health—and so are times of quiet meditation. Meditation decreases respiratory rate, increases blood flow, slows the heart rate, increases exercise tolerance, leads to a deeper level of relaxation, reduces blood pressure, and improves mood. Yoga or other mind-body exercise approaches combine the benefits of both movement and creating a quiet space that allows checking in with body and spirit.

— DAILY HEALTH JOURNAL —

Number of steps...............
O Add 2,000 steps

O Add 3 servings of vegetables
O Add 3 glasses of water

Six weeks of devotions for body and spirit **29**

On the Stormy Sea

MARK 4:35-39

*He woke up and rebuked the wind,
and said to the sea, "Peace! Be still."*
—Mark 4:39

AFTER A LONG DAY OF TEACHING, Jesus was tired. Leaving the crowd on the shore of the Sea of Galilee, Jesus' disciples took him in a boat to cross to the other side. Because the lake sat in a basin surrounded by mountains, changes in conditions could be swift. Winds swept down from the mountains and stirred up perilous swells that made it difficult to keep a boat stable. Waves swamped the boat, and the disciples, some of whom were fisherman who knew the lake well, wrestled to keep the boat from capsizing.

And where was Jesus? Asleep. We can easily imagine that his friends expected him to at least wake up—how could anyone sleep through a fierce squall? Once awake, hopefully Jesus would do something. He'd been doing miracles all around the countryside. Surely he could keep them safe. Yet he slept on until the disciples woke him up. Their demand is, "Don't you care that we're perishing?"

Sometimes, when we're swamped by our own storms of life, it feels like Jesus doesn't care. The disciples struggled with believing that Jesus brought the kingdom of God while in the moment it seemed as if they would not live long enough to see it.

Jesus woke up and calmed the storm. God is aware, present, and caring no matter what storms we face. What might be your storm today? Know that God's kingdom power is sufficient.

HEALTH TIP

After working hard all day, Jesus was weary, and he went to the stern of the boat and fell asleep. Most adults need seven to eight hours of sleep per night. Being chronically sleep-deprived suppresses your immune system. Sleep deprivation is scientifically linked to multiple medical conditions, including depression, nighttime heartburn, diabetes, hypertension, and heart disease. Arrange your busy life to allow time for sufficient rest.

— DAILY HEALTH JOURNAL —

Number of steps ....
O Add 2,000 steps

O Add 3 servings of vegetables
O Add 3 glasses of water

In the Gerasenes

MARK 5:1-4, 14-19

*"Go home to your friends, and tell them
how much the Lord has done for you."*
—Mark 5:19

JESUS HAD JUST CALMED a stormy sea and brought his disciples safely to shore. As soon as he stepped out of the boat, a man with an unclean spirit met him. It seems that everyone who knew him was terrified; he was strong enough to break shackles into pieces. Jesus healed the man by sending the spirits into a herd of pigs. When Jesus was getting back into the boat, the man begged to go along, but Jesus sent him home to his friends and family with a testimony of what God could do. The man's life was a wreck and now he was healed!

Most of us can come up with a list of things we wish had gone more smoothly in our day or the last few weeks. We may even be facing significant issues not just in our days but in our lives, sometimes for years at a time. We don't choose illness or grief or struggle. We want things to be put right—healed.

When we feel beyond help, Jesus helps. Jesus' instruction to the man he healed was to go home and tell his friends what God has done. We offer hope and healing to one another when we share our stories. All the stories matter, not just the most dramatic. Sharing our stories builds connections and helps us feel less alone in the struggle. We each have a story to tell, but we each also have many stories to hear.

HEALTH TIP

"Go home to your friends," Jesus said. Who do you look forward to seeing at the end of your day? Connecting with family and friends is vital to overall health. Too often we give the people who matter most the least of ourselves. Speak aloud the names of the people closest to you, and with each name think of a way to give to that person the best of yourself, rather than the leftovers.

— DAILY HEALTH JOURNAL —

Number of steps ....
○ Add 2,000 steps

○ Add 3 servings of vegetables
○ Add 3 glasses of water

Six weeks of devotions for body and spirit **31**

Week Two in Review

THE LAND JESUS TRAVELED was filled with natural beauty and scenic terrain. Jesus walked in grain fields, up the mountains, and along the seaside. Can you envision the area with its exotic trees and lush flowering plants? The Jordan River is a picturesque area that has many tree-lined offshoots. From the Dead Sea—the lowest place on earth—to the rocky terrain of Mt. Carmel, the diverse scenery of the land Jesus walked lent itself to being a spectacular backdrop for the unusual and inspiring events of Jesus' ministry.

Try to vary your physical activity opportunities. Varying your forms of exercise breaks up the monotony of a routine and helps you stay connected to your surroundings. Get outside some of the time to let the beauty of nature touch your spirit. As exercise becomes more a part of your usual day, you may find yourself less focused on the movement and more focused on the world around you.

Transfer your daily steps in the space below. If you set a goal for all three categories, put checkmarks in the boxes where you reached your goal for each day.

Number of steps	Add 2,000 steps	Add 3 vegetables	Add 3 glasses of water
Day 1	○	○	○
Day 2	○	○	○
Day 3	○	○	○
Day 4	○	○	○
Day 5	○	○	○
Day 6	○	○	○
Day 7	○	○	○

Nazareth Rejects Jesus

MARK 6:1-4

"Prophets are not without honor, except in their hometown,
and among their own kin, and in their own house."
—Mark 6:4

JESUS HAS ARRIVED IN HIS hometown of Nazareth. As he had done in other places, on the Sabbath he went to the synagogue to teach. There, essentially he was accused of trying to show off and reminded that he was just a carpenter from a small village, so he was no better than the people who had watched him grow up. He was a common worker like everyone else. Mark says "they took offense at him" despite acknowledging the wisdom of his teaching and the miracles he performed.

This is an interesting contrast to Mark's repeated mentions of the crowds who followed Jesus and were astounded by his words and deeds. Jesus shook off the rejection, saying, "Prophets are not without honor, except in their hometown, and among their own kin."

Sometimes people closest to us are not the ones who support the change and healing we pursue. Even if we clearly are successful in developing healthier habits, losing weight, or controlling cholesterol or blood sugar levels, not everyone is happy for us or interested in hearing the encouraging message we may be eager to share. Doing what God gives us to do may mean adjusting expectations while still honoring relationships.

Those who doubt our efforts to be healthy are not the voices we should tune into. We can listen to God's call to wholeness while being always ready to tell our stories when the time and place are right.

HEALTH TIP

Not everyone lives close to their parents, children, siblings, or extended family. Distance may weaken emotional bonds. And if not everyone gets along in ways that support health and well-being, family becomes more of a strain than a help. If you find yourself in a situation like this, don't think of yourself as not having family. Rather, find "chosen" family—the people around you with whom you share affection and support by choice.

— DAILY HEALTH JOURNAL —

Number of steps........................   ○ Add 3 servings of vegetables

○ Add 2,000 steps   ○ Add 3 glasses of water

The Hungry Crowd
MARK 6:30-43

*As he went ashore, he saw a great crowd;
and he had compassion for them.*
—Mark 6:34

THE STORY IN MARK 6 of Jesus feeding more than 5,000 people is one of the most well known among gospel accounts. Jesus actually was trying to get away from the crowds with his disciples so they could all rest and eat. Once again they journeyed by boat, but simultaneously the crowds raced around the shore line and were ready for him.

In the disciples' eyes, it was too late in the day to do anything more for the people. They could always start fresh the next day. All Jesus had to do was send the people away, and the disciples would get the rest they craved.

Moved with compassion, Jesus surprised everyone by telling the disciples to feed the crowd. "With what?" they wondered. Food for more than 5,000 people without any planning? "Figure it out," Jesus said, in essence.

Jesus took one boy's lunch and turned it into food for more than 5,000—with plenty of leftovers. This is a lesson of compassion leading to abundance. When we are tempted to conclude we don't have enough to share, or we don't have the energy to care about someone else's need—or we would like it if everyone would just go home—this story reminds us of what God can do with even our meager offerings of tangible goods, and our meager offering of uncertain faith. Maybe we can be a little slower to conclude that we simply can't help, offer what we have, and open our hearts to God's abundance.

HEALTH TIP
Jesus often used symbols from agriculture in his teaching. In biblical times, a well-fed people were blessed by a generous supply of grain—wheat, barley, millet, and corn. Diets rich in whole grains help to reduce the risk of cancers of the digestive tract and lungs, along with heart disease. For a few days, keep track of the breads and grains you eat. How many of them are whole grain?

— DAILY HEALTH JOURNAL —

Number of steps........................   ○ Add 3 servings of vegetables
○ Add 2,000 steps   ○ Add 3 glasses of water

Walking on Water to Bethsaida

MARK 6:45–51

"Take heart, it is I; do not be afraid."
—Mark 6:50

AFTER FEEDING MORE THAN 5,000 people, Jesus sent the disciples ahead in a boat to the other side of the lake while he dismissed the large crowd and took some time alone for prayer. The disciples again had a rough crossing, but in this story Jesus was not in the boat. They could not simply wake him to plead for help. The boat had left the shore "when evening came" (Mark 6:47), and hours later, "early in the morning" (Mark 6:48), they were still straining against the wind.

They must have been exhausted—and tense. It was dark and windy, with swells of waves impeding progress across the lake. Is it any wonder that the disciples in the boat had trouble making sense of seeing a figure walking toward them *on* the water? How was this possible? If they were not already frightened, this sight terrified them.

We all know the sensation of fear, of danger, of imminent harm. Our lives are full of deep waters that we must navigate, sometimes for far longer than we think we can manage. Emotionally we can put ourselves in the boat with the disciples.

"Take heart," Jesus said, "it is I; do not be afraid." Just as the disciples had difficulty recognizing Jesus' presence in the storm, we, too, need reassurance that Jesus is with us. Jesus showed up in a way the disciples did not expect, and he does the same for us.

HEALTH TIP

If you struggle with anxiety, you are not alone. Anxiety disorders affect 40 million adults in the US, making it the most common mental health disorder. But when it happens to you, it's personal, not just a national statistic. Simple efforts make a difference. Take a time-out. Put on some favorite music. Prioritize regular exercise. Protect your sleep. Seek out humor. Talk to someone you trust about how you feel.

— DAILY HEALTH JOURNAL —

Number of steps............................. ◯ Add 3 servings of vegetables

◯ Add 2,000 steps ◯ Add 3 glasses of water

Passing by Sidon

MARK 7:31–35

*They brought to him a deaf man who had an impediment
in his speech; and they begged him to lay his hand on him.*
—Mark 7:32

A S JESUS CONTINUED TO minister, the sick and injured continued to come to him. One day a deaf man with a speech impediment was brought to him. Mark has already given us several images of the role of touch in Jesus' healing work (3:10, 5:27–28, 5:41, 6:56), and the man's friends now begged Jesus to touch a man who was deaf and could hardly speak in order to heal him. Jesus responded by touching the man in ways clearly related to the conditions that made his life difficult—his ears were opened and his tongue released (7:35).

Mark opened his Gospel with Jesus announcing that "the kingdom of God has come near." Now this healing story echoes the words of an Old Testament picture of the redeeming work of God: "Then the eyes of the blind shall be opened, and the ears of the deaf unstopped; then the lame shall leap like a deer, and the tongue of the speechless sing for joy" (Isaiah 35:5–6).

We don't know who made up the "they" who brought the deaf man to Jesus, but we see clearly that they believed Jesus could heal him. Sometimes we think "they" should do something about a social problem, or "they" should do something to help someone in need. As we look for ourselves in this story, let's see that "they" were the ordinary people who made a difference. The kingdom has indeed come near, and we are part of showing it to the world.

HEALTH TIP

Helping others, like the people in the Bible passage did, is good for your health. People who volunteer feel better mentally, physically, and emotionally, and this helps manage stress. Volunteering also wards off loneliness and builds important social connections that sustain mental health. Other benefits include a greater level of happiness, which may be linked to longer lifespan, lower blood pressure, and better pain management.

— DAILY HEALTH JOURNAL —

Number of steps ....   ◯ Add 3 servings of vegetables
◯ Add 2,000 steps   ◯ Add 3 glasses of water

Blindness in Bethsaida
MARK 8:22-25

*Jesus laid his hands on his eyes again; and he
looked intently and his sight was restored.*
—Mark 8:25

AGAIN IN TODAY'S PASSAGE we see Mark's emphasis on other people bringing to Jesus individuals who need healing, a nudge that reminds us that we pursue health and wholeness alongside other people. In the previous chapter we read about a man who was deaf and mute, which hearkened back to Isaiah 35. This time it is a man who is blind. Healing of the blind fits right in with descriptions of Jesus doing the redeeming work God promised through Isaiah—"The eyes of the blind shall be opened" (Isaiah 35:5).

And also once again we see Jesus' method of healing by touching. First he led the blind man by the hand, and then he touched his eyes twice.

One interesting angle in this story is that when Jesus healed the man's sight, Mark did not simply tell us the man could see. He unfolds for us the process of finding clarity of vision. The man's perspective on the world shifted and came into focus as he was healed.

Sometimes seeing a different perspective is the first step toward health change. The beginning of our healing may be learning to see ourselves differently and truly know that God loves us. The new perspective might be to see hope and potential that was shrouded before because now we have found support in forming new habits. And once our own eyes are opened, we can help lead others to the healing Jesus offers as well.

HEALTH TIP

If you need to go out to lunch for work or with a friend, when you order, ask for a "to go" box to take home. Most restaurants serve portion sizes much larger than recommended. Control portion size by putting half of your order in the box before you begin to eat. Put the box out of sight and savor the meal knowing you can enjoy the flavors again later.

— DAILY HEALTH JOURNAL —

Number of steps............

○ Add 2,000 steps

○ Add 3 servings of vegetables

○ Add 3 glasses of water

DAY 20

On the High Mountain

MARK 9:2-8

Then a cloud overshadowed them, and from the cloud
there came a voice, "This is my Son, the Beloved; listen to him."
—Mark 9:7

TODAY'S PASSAGE RECOUNTS an event known as the Transfiguration. Jesus took Peter, James, and John up on a mountain, and they saw him become dazzlingly, blindingly bright. Peter stumbled around for the right response to mark the glory of that moment. Mark tells us that Peter didn't really know what to say because the disciples were so frightened by this vision.

"Mountaintop" experiences take us out of the shadows of our usual lives and give us a glimpse of God's glory in our lives, even if we're not sure what to make of them. Just like Peter, we want to mark them in some way to help us grasp their significance and let our spirits linger in the glory.

Still, we have to go down off the mountain into the work God gives us to do. The best thing we carry with us as we go down are the words Jesus' friends heard on the mountain: "This is my Son, the Beloved; listen to him!"

God spoke similar words at Jesus' baptism: "You are my son, the Beloved; with you I am well pleased" (Mark 1:11). God's love for Jesus, the Son of God, is what drives Jesus forward in the work he came into the world to accomplish so that humans can know and experience the kingdom of God. God's love also sustains and propels us forward in the work of better health for ourselves and others in both body and spirit.

HEALTH TIP

Love has healing powers. It values, encourages, affirms, cherishes. Jot down a quick list of people in your life who would be encouraged to know they are in your thoughts and heart. Then brainstorm some quick ways to spread the love through short e-mails, photos, quick notes, phone calls, humorous voice mail messages, or surprise text messages. Brightening someone else's day will also brighten yours, leading to lower stress and more positive mental outlook.

— **DAILY HEALTH JOURNAL** —

Number of steps............................   ○ Add 3 servings of vegetables
○ Add 2,000 steps   ○ Add 3 glasses of water

Down from the Mountain

MARK 9:14–29

Immediately the father of the child cried out,
"I believe; help my unbelief."
—Mark 9:24

JESUS'S REENTRY TO MINISTRY after the mountaintop Transfiguration experience was abrupt. He walked straight into an argument about why his disciples were unable to heal an individual with a spirit that caused him to convulse. When the young man's father presented him to Jesus, Jesus asked how long the convulsions had been going on. "From childhood," came the answer in a plea for pity. The father in this story was desperate for someone to care. While the disciples were arguing with the religious leaders, the father's mind was on his son. Was it possible Jesus could do what his disciples could not?

Jesus said, "All things can be done for the one who believes," and the man responded, "I believe; help my unbelief!"

Faith allows us to avoid setting limits on our expectations for how much God cares about our troubles. But human faith is never perfect or unfailing. Many of us can well identify with the declaration of the father. Jesus entered a scene full of chaos and took charge. The son needed healing of his affliction, and the father needed healing of his faith. Jesus offered both.

Belief and unbelief are a mixed bag, even when it comes to whether we think we can make health changes and whether God cares enough to help. Under no circumstances can we create faith within ourselves, but we can ask God for faith and open ourselves to receive it as a first step to healing in body and spirit.

HEALTH TIP

When we try to live a life of faith on our own, most of the time doubt creeps in. Is our faith strong enough? Do we really understand the Bible? Are we disappointing God? Keep in mind that the church is the body of Christ, and everyone has a part in the body. We need each other. One of the gifts we exchange is walking the road of faith together. Who can help your unbelief?

— DAILY HEALTH JOURNAL —

Number of steps.................   ◯ Add 3 servings of vegetables
◯ Add 2,000 steps   ◯ Add 3 glasses of water

Week Three in Review

DO YOU KNOW YOUR family health history? Does your family have a history of heart disease, cancer, arthritis, or other illness? Take some time at the next family gathering to get to know your family health history. This information will be a good companion to your health goals.

We are at the halfway point in six weeks of *Walking with Jesus*, which is a good time to reevaluate progress toward your goals. Do you need to give yourself some grace? More challenge? More healthy celebration of what you have achieved so far? What habits do you want to work on with more intention?

Take time now to total your weekly steps and jot down one main goal you want to work on for the final three weeks of the program.

Transfer your daily steps in the space below. If you set a goal for all three categories, put checkmarks in the boxes where you reached your goal for each day.

Number of steps	Add 2,000 steps	Add 3 vegetables	Add 3 glasses of water
Day 1	O	O	O
Day 2	O	O	O
Day 3	O	O	O
Day 4	O	O	O
Day 5	O	O	O
Day 6	O	O	O
Day 7	O	O	O

Coming to Capernaum
MARK 9:33–37

"Whoever wants to be first must be
last of all and servant to all."
—Mark 9:35

HAVE YOU EVER ASKED a group of children what they're squabbling about and received the reply, "Nothing!" What had seemed important enough to quarrel over is put into perspective when a parent or teacher comes on the scene. This dynamic happened with Jesus and his disciples. He knew they were arguing, but they didn't want him to know the topic: who was the greatest? It must have been embarrassing. Of course Jesus knew anyway, and he used a small child to make the point that in the kingdom of God humility is more powerful than greatness.

Why are we so stuck on being the greatest? The athlete with the best record. The student with the best grades. The youngest person to hold a high-level position in the company. The highest performing employee. The most popular person.

Some people achieve to fulfill personal goals. But too often we get swept up in competition because we seek recognition from others. We must ask ourselves why we feel so insecure that we want others to believe what we don't believe for ourselves—that we have value, that we matter, that we are making a contribution.

Where is our true worth? Not in what we achieve or the recognition others offer, but in humbly welcoming Jesus and those he came to serve. Other people matter, and we walk together toward wholeness when we serve each other in humility rather than relating in competition.

HEALTH TIP

Olive oil was a staple in Jesus' time. It was used for a variety of purposes—food, seasoning, preservative, economic barter, lighting lamps. Today we understand the olive oil has more monounsaturated fats than other vegetable oils. These fats may help lower "bad" cholesterol while raising "good" cholesterol, which in turn reduces the risk of heart disease. We don't use it for lighting lamps anymore, but it's a great choice for cooking.

— DAILY HEALTH JOURNAL —

Number of steps.................

O Add 2,000 steps

O Add 3 servings of vegetables

O Add 3 glasses of water

Beyond the Jordan

MARK 10:13-16

*"Let the little children come to me; do not stop them; for it
is to such as these that the kingdom of God belongs."*
—Mark 10:14

MARK HAS TOLD US BEFORE that people brought those who were ill to Jesus and wanted him to touch them. Today's passage does not say the children brought to Jesus were ill, but they might have been. Or, perhaps people recognized Jesus' touch of wellness and blessing even in the absence of illness.

The disciples had a stern reaction, as if they were ranking some people as more deserving of Jesus' attention and children were at the bottom of the list. Jesus, however, chastised not the weak but those who put themselves in a position of authority. Mark describes him as "indignant." Then he put children forth as an example for everyone who wishes to participate in the kingdom of God. From children we learn the joy of exploring, learning, and interacting with the world around us—the world God created and put us in. This is how we should receive the kingdom of God. The lesson comes from an unexpected source—small children—but it is meant for all of us.

The health of children in their earliest years can set the trajectory for their lifespans. Not everyone is a parent, but everyone sees and knows children. In schools, parks, stores, churches, community centers, family gatherings, we all have opportunity to touch the lives of children. When we recognize their worth and open ourselves to learning from them even as we care for them, we share in Jesus' blessing of the children.

HEALTH TIP

Obese children as young as seven may already have the beginnings of artery disease. Carotid arteries may already be thick and stiff. Children may also have a higher risk of diabetes. Children can be picky eaters, but repeated exposure to a wider range of food options—healthy balanced nutrition—can gradually lead to children independently choosing for themselves. When parents take the lead and set an example, children notice.

— DAILY HEALTH JOURNAL —

Number of steps............................   O Add 3 servings of vegetables

O Add 2,000 steps   O Add 3 glasses of water

Setting Out on a Journey

MARK 10:17-22

Jesus, looking at him, loved him and said, "You lack one thing; go, sell what you own, and give the money to the poor, and you will have treasure in heaven; then come, follow me."

—Mark 10:21

A WEALTHY MAN ASKED JESUS how he could inherit eternal life. He was on a spiritual quest, but he had his own conceptions of the answer he sought. He wanted to know what to *do*, even though he was already doing a great deal by keeping the commandments of the Old Testament. "I have kept all these since my youth," the man said. Perhaps he was also keeping all the rules and regulations that the Pharisees added on to the Old Testament law.

It's hard to know what the man was hoping Jesus would say. Perhaps Jesus would add a new law, and the man would follow that one as well. But Jesus could see that the man needed to think more deeply about the changes he was prepared to make in his life.

"Go, sell what you own," Jesus said, "and give the money to the poor, and you will have treasure in heaven; then come, follow me."

We might think that the man, if he truly wanted eternal life, would have been willing to do anything. Instead, he went away in grief. Jesus was asking too much.

We all have possessions or habits that we hold dear. Are we willing to give up something that's part of the life we're used to in order to gain the life we'd like to have? Making a new healthy habit means letting go of an old one, and that can be the hardest first step to take.

HEALTH TIP

What kind of food do you like to eat? What dishes are the hardest for you to pass up even if you know they don't line up with your goals for better nutrition? You can enjoy favorite foods in two ways. First, move them to the category of occasional treats, rather than mainstays in your diet. Second, search for recipes that adapt favorite foods by preparing them with fresh ingredients and lower fat.

— DAILY HEALTH JOURNAL —

Number of steps ....
O Add 2,000 steps

O Add 3 servings of vegetables
O Add 3 glasses of water

Toward Jerusalem

MARK 10:35-37, 41-45

"For the Son of Man came not to be served but to serve, and to give his life a ransom for many."
—Mark 10:45

J AMES AND JOHN, who were among the first disciples Jesus called to follow him, somehow got it in their heads that they should be elevated to positions of prestige in the kingdom that Jesus was bringing. One would sit at Jesus' right hand, and the other on the left.

Jesus did not grant the prideful request. Nevertheless, when the other ten disciples discovered that James and John had been so audacious, their hackles were raised. What did James and John think they were doing? Why should they have special treatment?

The truth is that at some moments we all think we deserve special treatment. That "No Parking" sign shouldn't apply to us. People with less experience should defer to our decisions. We're in a hurry, so we should be able to go to the front of the line. Often the issues are not very big ones, yet we still think we should have special treatment regardless of how it makes others feel.

When we focus on our own sense of deserving, we miss the opportunity to serve. We overlook the reality that our sense of deserving more means someone else deserves less. Even in small ways, we contribute to division and dissension. Jesus reminded his disciples of a life of service that benefits many others. The same lesson is meant for us. This is what Jesus did, and this is what Jesus calls us to do.

HEALTH TIP

Know the signs of a heart attack: chest pain that feels like squeezing, pressure, or pain; pain or discomfort in the jaw, back, neck, arms, or stomach; shortness of breath; cold sweat and nausea or lightheadedness. Today brush up on the symptoms of major health events that could threaten you or someone you encounter.

— DAILY HEALTH JOURNAL —

Number of steps .... ○ Add 3 servings of vegetables
○ Add 2,000 steps   ○ Add 3 glasses of water

Arriving in Jericho
MARK 10:46-52

*When he heard that it was Jesus of Nazareth, he began
to shout out and say, "Jesus, Son of David, have mercy on me!"*
—Mark 10:47

J ESUS WAS ON HIS WAY TO Jerusalem to face the final week of his life. His route took him through Jericho. Herod the Great had rebuilt the ancient city of Old Testament times, and it was once again a thriving place. Beggars along public roads were common. When Bartimaeus, who was blind and subsisted by begging, heard that Jesus was coming through town, he called out for mercy.

The crowd around Bartimaeus shushed him. They preferred that he be silent, invisible. But Bartimaeus knew that the nearness of Jesus was an opportunity for healing. Jesus heard him. Rather than expect Bartimaeus to be silent, Jesus engaged him in conversation about his desire for healing. When Jesus left, Bartimaeus had his sight.

Perhaps you know what it feels like for other people to look past you, to not acknowledge your place in the community, to push you aside for someone more "worthy." Or perhaps you have been the one to look past someone in need, to sidestep someone who just doesn't fit into your social circle or the way you've arranged your life.

In truth, we all do it. We look through people all the time as if they weren't there or because we don't want them to be there. But Jesus gave his time and attention to the lowly once again. It is worth asking ourselves every day how we will follow Jesus' example to care for the most vulnerable among us.

HEALTH TIP

For most of us, mornings are a rushed routine to get everybody out the door. Although some occupations are performed outdoors, most are not. We go from inside the house to inside a school or place of employment. We rarely take the time during the day to bask in the sun. Today, celebrate the sun as it gives energy to your life. Even a few minutes in the sun provides Vitamin D essential to health.

— DAILY HEALTH JOURNAL —

Number of steps................................   ○ Add 3 servings of vegetables
○ Add 2,000 steps   ○ Add 3 glasses of water

Arriving in Jerusalem

MARK 11:1-11

"Blessed is the coming kingdom of our ancestor
David! Hosanna in the highest heaven!"
—Mark 11:10

IN THE FINAL DAYS BEFORE Jesus' death, Jerusalem was crowded. Jewish believers came from all over the Roman Empire to celebrate the Passover feast. Jesus was traveling to Jerusalem for the same reason. When he was about two miles away from the city, he sent his disciples for a colt that had never been ridden. The Old Testament prophet Zechariah wrote that "your king will come to you" riding on a colt (Zechariah 9:9).

Jesus told his disciples that if anyone asked why they were taking the colt, they should say, "The LORD needs it." Jesus may have arranged ahead of time to use the colt. We can see both that the colt was made available to Jesus and the confident obedience of the disciples. We might ask ourselves what we have that we can make available when the Lord needs it.

The scene that begins when Jesus rides the colt into Jerusalem matches what Zechariah described—God's kingdom comes, and the people rejoice. "Hosanna in the highest heaven!" the people shout. *Hosanna* is a word used in songs of praise, especially on Palm Sunday when we celebrate Jesus' entrance to Jerusalem. But it also is a cry of "save us," a fitting meaning for us to remember as Jesus moves through the coming days toward crucifixion. With our cry of "Hosanna" we welcome the salvation Jesus brings.

HEALTH TIP

While some stress is good, too much stress in your life over a long period time can have negative health effects. Meditation and prayer can be effective ways to reduce the impact of stress. Something as simple as spending a minute or two focused on taking deep, full breaths can have a positive effect. Be aware of when your body is telling you it is overloaded, and give yourself a time-out from the pressure of the day.

--- **DAILY HEALTH JOURNAL** ---

Number of steps............................   ○ Add 3 servings of vegetables
○ Add 2,000 steps   ○ Add 3 glasses of water

Teaching in the Temple

MARK 11:15–19

"My house shall be called a house of prayer for all the nations."
—Mark 11:17

WHEN SOMEONE REFERS TO Jesus "cleansing the temple," we think of overturned tables and righteous anger. We don't think of teaching. Yet Mark tells us that Jesus was teaching (Mark 11:17). Jesus went into Jerusalem for the Passover feast along with throngs of Jews from around the Roman Empire. It's easy to imagine how crowded the temple must have been. Pilgrims from beyond the immediate region needed to purchase animals that met the requirements of the law for purity in order to offer sacrifices. This is why we read of animal pens in the temple. Also, the temple tax had to be paid in local currency, so moneychangers set up their booths as well.

This was big business! The problem was that all this business was conducted in the only part of the temple where God-fearing Gentiles were allowed to worship and pray. It would seem that the culture of the time had come to accept this status quo—convenience for traveling Jews and profits for business people—at the expense of the Gentiles who genuinely sought to worship God.

After driving out the profiteers, Jesus quoted from Isaiah 56:6–7 to remind listeners that the house of God is for all people. A question for us to ponder is: In what ways do we accept the status quo and get in the way of others seeking God? And are we willing to be part of change?

HEALTH TIP

Do you have a favorite Bible verse or prayer that helps anchor your faith life, even in times of change and upheaval? Write out the words of the verse or prayer on a card you can put up where you can see it. Then make another copy to share with a friend or coworker who needs some encouragement or reassurance of God's presence.

— DAILY HEALTH JOURNAL —

Number of steps............................
O Add 2,000 steps

O Add 3 servings of vegetables
O Add 3 glasses of water

Week Four in Review

MAKING CHANGES IN HEALTH habits often focus on movement and nutrition, because we often define *health* as the state of our physical bodies. But while activity and nutrition are important, they are not the only pieces to living a healthy life. Don't overlook making changes in your spiritual practices that will support your resolution to move toward a healthier, more fulfilled life. Friends and family also play key roles.

As you look back on the week you just finished and forward to the new week, what small changes might you want to make in your faith life? Do you want to worship more? Listen to uplifting music? Share your heart with a close friend? Chose one goal, write it down, and make a plan for how you can accomplish it in the coming week.

Transfer your daily steps in the space below. If you set a goal for all three categories, put checkmarks in the boxes where you reached your goal for each day.

Number of steps	Add 2,000 steps	Add 3 vegetables	Add 3 glasses of water
Day 1	○	○	○
Day 2	○	○	○
Day 3	○	○	○
Day 4	○	○	○
Day 5	○	○	○
Day 6	○	○	○
Day 7	○	○	○

First of All: Love

MARK 12:28-34

"You shall love the Lord your God with all your heart, and with all your soul, and with all your mind, and with all your strength"
—Mark 12:30

SINCE ENTERING JERUSALEM for the last week before his death, Jesus has been debating the recognized religious leaders in a series of questions intended to corner him into saying something that would dismantle the authority that the crowds have seen in him since the beginning of his ministry. Is it right to pay taxes to Caesar? (Mark 12:14). If seven brothers were all married to the same woman because they all died without leaving children, who will be her husband at the resurrection? (Mark 12:23). And in today's passage, "Which commandment is the first of all?" (Mark 12:28).

The religious leaders of the time counted more than 600 commandments in the Hebrew scriptures. Was it even right to choose among them? Jesus' answer to the scribe's question took the listening crowd straight back to the center of their faith, the "Shema" first written in Deuteronomy 6:4. *Shema* means "hear." The first commandment is to love God, Jesus said, and the second to love others.

Love for others is an essential expression of our love for God. Just as it was more important than the burnt offerings at the heart of Jewish worship, it is still a truer manifestation of our faith than what we do inside the walls of a church.

What God asks of us is loyalty to the kingdom that has come near that we express in compassion. The command to love God and neighbor are connected. Who loves you? Who needs your love?

HEALTH TIP

We often expect perfection of ourselves. The trouble with such expectations is that we simply are not perfect, and falling short of perfection can become demoralizing. Friends and family can help. Fall back on the people who love you even when you might not like yourself very well. They may even be willing to help you accomplish a project that would get you back on track. Getting things done is a great way to bond.

— DAILY HEALTH JOURNAL —

Number of steps........................   ○ Add 3 servings of vegetables
○ Add 2,000 steps   ○ Add 3 glasses of water

Opposite the Treasury

MARK 12:41-44

*"Truly I tell you, this poor widow has put in more than
all those who are contributing to the treasury."*
—Mark 12:43

MARK OFFERS US ANOTHER story of Jesus at the temple during the busy season of the Passover Feast when travelers came from all over the empire to observe Jewish tradition as outlined in the Law of Moses. Some of these journeys would have been at considerable expense, requiring sacrifice in order to participate in the feast.

Jesus was crowd-watching. He'd already seen the merchants profiting off religious observance. He'd already debated the best religious thinkers of his time. Now he sat down across from the temple treasury and watched people dropping money into the containers set up for this purpose. "Many rich people put in large sums," Mark tells us (12:41). But these were not the people who interested Jesus. A widow put in two small coins worth so little they would hardly be worth picking up off the ground.

Jesus did not call his disciples to come and see the generosity of the rich. Rather, he explained that this poor widow had put in more than all the others.

Sometimes we think we have nothing to offer. We don't have the bank account of someone else, or the speaking ability, or the musical talent. We're not leaders of Fortune 500 companies. But Jesus noticed the gift of someone marginalized in her society, and he notices us. When we give back to God the gifts God has given to us, that is true generosity. Given out of sacrifice, our small gifts make a great difference.

HEALTH TIP

When was the last time you cleaned out your medicine cabinet? Many accidents can be avoided by disposing of expired medications or those you no longer need to take. A tidier cabinet will make it easier to find the things you do need. And something as simple as accomplishing this task can help build a sense of control that can carry over into other goals you've set as you form new health habits.

--- **DAILY HEALTH JOURNAL** ---

Number of steps......................   ◯ Add 3 servings of vegetables
◯ Add 2,000 steps   ◯ Add 3 glasses of water

WEEK FIVE

DAY 31

With Friends in Bethany

MARK 14:3-9

"For you always have the poor with you, and you can show kindness to them whenever you wish."

—Mark 14:7

THE PLOT TO KILL JESUS intensified, yet he continued steadfast in his own ministry. Once again Mark shows us Jesus associating with the marginalized. We've seen his value of children, tax collectors, sinners, the poor, and now a "leper." That Simon the leper was in his own home hosting a meal suggests he had been healed of an ostracizing disease, likely by Jesus.

During the meal, a woman poured expensive perfume over Jesus' head—not just a spritz, but the full jar. Some of the disciples objected to this poignant, generous expression of devotion. They could have sold the jar, they said, and used the money for the poor. What she did was wasteful, they said.

Not surprising, Jesus rose to her defense and commended her. "You always have the poor with you," he said, "and you can show kindness to them whenever you wish" (Mark 14:7).

How easy it is to judge another person's action through our own lens, rather than seeing the action for what it is. We have our own ideas about how money should be used, how faith should be expressed, what constitutes true worship.

Jesus made the point that we don't have to choose between Jesus and being generous to the poor. Understanding that the poor will always be with us does not mean we should not offer resources to help the poor, but it does mean we have limitless opportunities to be kind to the poor.

HEALTH TIP

Whether you're heading to the park or traveling across the country, create a family First Aid Kit stocked with the basics for minor injuries: bandages, antibiotic cream, pain relievers, gauze, first aid tape, scissors, tweezers, alcohol swabs, hand sanitizer, and an elastic bandage. A flashlight, blanket, and container of water in the car are also good ideas, and don't forget to keep your emergency numbers handy.

— DAILY HEALTH JOURNAL —

Number of steps ....
O Add 2,000 steps

O Add 3 servings of vegetables
O Add 3 glasses of water

In the Upper Room

MARK 14:12-16

So the disciples set out and went to the city, and found everything just as he had told them; and they prepared the Passover meal.
—Mark 14:16

AS THE FEAST WEEK MOVES TOWARD its climax, Jesus and his closest disciples make plans to observe Passover together. Nowadays we talk about the "upper room" in a way that encompasses significant events on the final full day of Jesus' life before crucifixion—Jesus, the master, taking on the servant role of washing his disciples' feet; the "new commandment" to love one another; the revelation that one of the disciples would soon betray Jesus to religious authorities; the meal itself; the meaning Jesus gave to the "new covenant."

It all began when Jesus sent his disciples to find the room. Preparation also would have included gathering the food—unleavened bread, bitter herbs, a lamb, wine. Many homes had stairs on the outside leading up to large rooms on the roof that could be offered for hospitality or for use by people outside the family. Jesus gave specific instructions how his disciples would find this upper room.

Jesus sent the disciples to prepare for the festival meal, but he was the one in charge of the meaning it would take on. While remembering the Israelite's exodus from Egypt centuries earlier, Jesus used the occasion to prepare his friends for what was to come—beginning before the night was over. The weekend's transition through death to life again would herald once again that the kingdom of God was near.

HEALTH TIP

The Israelites spent many hours preparing and making bread for the table. Jesus made preparation for the Last Supper. Take time to plan and prepare your table. Do you have a well-balanced meal including healthy portions, fruits and vegetables, milk products, protein, and healthy fat? Take time to prepare food to nourish your body and invite others to the table to nourish your spirit.

— DAILY HEALTH JOURNAL —

Number of steps...............................   ◯ Add 3 servings of vegetables

◯ Add 2,000 steps   ◯ Add 3 glasses of water

Around the Last Table

MARK 14:22-26

He said to them, "This is my blood of the covenant, which is poured out for many."
—Mark 14:24

PASSING THE BREAD AND DRINKING the wine are two traditional parts of the Passover meal. When Jesus broke bread and drank wine with his closest disciples, he infused new meaning into the common actions of the feast they had been celebrating all their lives. By this time Judas had already made his arrangements to betray Jesus for a payment in silver coins (Mark 14:10–11), yet he sits at the table with the others. The Passover meal would have recounted the story of Israel's exodus from Egypt.

Jesus blessed the bread, broke it, and said, "This is my body." Then he gave thanks for the cup bearing the fruit of the vine and said, "This is my blood of the covenant, which is poured out for many." Knowing that his betrayer was among them, and that the events to come would bring his death, Jesus nevertheless gave thanks.

Mark focuses on Jesus' words and the meaning of the "new covenant." Jesus was about to offer himself as the spotless lamb of God. At the conclusion of the meal, they sang a hymn and went to the Mount of Olives. How much did the disciples understand as they followed Jesus there? Were they talking among themselves about what Jesus meant when he offered them the body and wine with new meaning? Jesus was carrying out his kingdom mission, and even in his last hours the disciples were learning what that meant.

HEALTH TIP

We must remember that we are whole people, beloved by God, for whom Jesus sacrificed himself. How do you breathe in the midst of crises, loss, grief, anxiety, sickness, and busyness? Learn to breathe in the breath of God in all your moments. As you take a deep breath, mentally form the words of a simple prayer for God's presence. To be well is to be in balance with God in all aspects of our lives.

— DAILY HEALTH JOURNAL —

Number of steps.............
O Add 2,000 steps

O Add 3 servings of vegetables
O Add 3 glasses of water

Gethsemane

MARK 14:32-42

*"Keep awake and pray that you may not come into the time
of trial; the spirit indeed is willing, but the flesh is weak."*

—Mark 14:38

"**T**HE SPIRIT IS WILLING,** but the flesh is weak," we sometimes banter as we pick up a frosted cookie with a sheepish grin. Many don't recognize that the source of the phrase is a somber experience.

In a garden called Gethsemane, Jesus took Peter, James, and John to a secluded place to pray. He asked them to stay awake while he threw himself on the ground asking God if there wasn't another way for God's will to be accomplished without requiring an agonizing death. We clearly see Jesus' humanity in this spiritual wrestling.

When he returned to Peter, James, and John, he found them sleeping. Three times this happened—Jesus asked them to remain awake and wait with him, went off to wrestle with what God has asked of him, and returned to find them asleep. "The spirit indeed is willing, but the flesh is weak" (Mark 14:38). Perhaps in his scolding of the disciples Jesus also reflected his own tension between his commitment to God's will and the request for another way to accomplish it.

In times of stress, we are vulnerable to temptation. Even for Jesus, this was a "time of trial." But all through the book of Mark we have seen Jesus as the master of the situation. Jesus was not taken by surprise. He knew what Judas was doing while Jesus was praying. And despite their failure to remain awake with him, Jesus took his disciples with him to face his arrest.

HEALTH TIP

Do you know that a morning meal rich in fiber may make you more alert during the day? Fiber may release fatty acids that create energy. The degree to which you feel sleepy or alert is not only related to how many hours you spend sleeping— eight is recommended—but also to the fuel you choose for your body, especially in the morning.

— DAILY HEALTH JOURNAL —

Number of steps................................ ○ Add 3 servings of vegetables

○ Add 2,000 steps   ○ Add 3 glasses of water

Arrested in the Garden

MARK 14:43–49

So when he came, he went up to him at once and said, "Rabbi!"
and kissed him. Then they laid hands on him and arrested him.
—Mark 14:45–46

J UDAS, ONE OF THE 12 closest friends of Jesus, now becomes Jesus' accuser, betraying with an intimate gesture of a kiss.

One of them—traditionally Peter—tried to protest, drawing his sword in an attempt to intercept the arrest. In the process he cut off the ear of a slave. Luke 22:51 gives us more detail about this incident, telling us Jesus immediately healed the man by touch. In one last act of healing ministry Jesus once again used touch as his healing method.

The soldiers who came to arrest Jesus were not Roman soldiers but members of the temple guard who served the Jewish religious leaders, rather than the Roman government. As Jesus pointed out, they could have arrested him any time they wanted to out in the public or even in the temple. Instead, they waited until they were in a secluded place.

Judas has top billing among the disciples in this story because he arranged the betrayal and accepted money to lead the religious leaders to Jesus even in seclusion. But Mark also tells us that the rest of the disciples fled and deserted Jesus.

The people closest to us can disappoint us. It's difficult to work through the feelings that follow. But our lives have greater purpose than what goes wrong. Even wrapped in abandonment, Jesus proceeded with what was necessary to bring near the kingdom of God.

HEALTH TIP

Although people may disappoint us, and we may even disappoint ourselves by falling short of our goals or demonstrating an attitude we regret, we can give ourselves and each other second and third and fourth chances. Create a "one-liner" to help you cultivate this goal, such as "Blessed are the flexible, for they shall not be bent out of shape." What is one sentence you'd like to remember as you move through this day?

— DAILY HEALTH JOURNAL —

Number of steps..................................   ○ Add 3 servings of vegetables
○ Add 2,000 steps   ○ Add 3 glasses of water

Week Five in Review

I N WHAT WAYS HAVE YOU noticed changes in your body and spirit over the past few weeks? Have you noticed the healing effects from exercise as you've increased your steps or found other activities you enjoy? Exercise can not only heal us mentally by soothing anger, stress, and anxiety, but also we might see changes in our bodies as we gain strength, endurance, and energy.

Using muscles breaks them down, and as they naturally repair, they become even stronger. Excess body fat, which can increase the risk of some diseases, is burned during exercise to provide fuel for your activity. How can you challenge yourself in the upcoming final week to grow, change, and heal even further?

Transfer your daily steps in the space below. If you set a goal for all three categories, put checkmarks in the boxes where you reached your goal for each day.

Number of steps	Add 2,000 steps	Add 3 vegetables	Add 3 glasses of water
Day 1	○	○	○
Day 2	○	○	○
Day 3	○	○	○
Day 4	○	○	○
Day 5	○	○	○
Day 6	○	○	○
Day 7	○	○	○

In the Courtyard

MARK 14:66-72

Then Peter remembered that Jesus had said to him, "Before the cock crows twice, you will deny me three times." And he broke down and wept.
—Mark 14:72

THE TEMPLE GUARD TOOK Jesus to the high priest, which was a spacious palace with multiple courtyards. Although Mark told us that all the disciples scattered when Jesus was arrested—perhaps for fear of what would happen to them—now he reveals that Peter was trying to keep track of what was happening to Jesus without being discovered. While Jesus was on trial for a trumped-up charge of blasphemy, Peter was trying to keep warm in a courtyard and listen for bits of information.

Perhaps if Peter had kept his head down better, his guise might have succeeded. But a female servant recognized him, and when he opened his mouth to say she was mistaken, he dug himself in deeper. His Galilean accent gave him away. He had to keep his story consistent, so three times he denied any association with Jesus.

Peter panicked and took the most direct action he could think of to save himself from the unknown. The words were hardly out of his mouth when the rooster crowed the second time—just as Jesus said would happen.

Sometimes others disappoint us. Sometimes we are the ones who let others down—and ourselves. We understand Peter's shame at what he did. What reassurance it is to know that Jesus walked forward with God's plan for our healing and salvation so that our moments of shame do not remove us from the dignity and value God created for us.

HEALTH TIP

Parenting is challenging and can increase daily stress that takes a toll on health—loss of sleep, the temptation to take nutritional short-cuts, putting exercise on the back burner, worry about a child's welfare. Whether parenting small children or young adults, take two minutes to stop and reflect on what you admire about your children and age-appropriate ways to communicate your thoughts. This can help keep you positively focused on the life-transforming role you play.

— DAILY HEALTH JOURNAL —

Number of steps.............................   ○ Add 3 servings of vegetables
○ Add 2,000 steps   ○ Add 3 glasses of water

Before Pilate

MARK 15:6–15

So Pilate, wishing to satisfy the crowd, released Barabbas for them;
and after flogging Jesus, he handed him over to be crucified.
—Mark 15:15

UNLIKE THE RELIGIOUS LEADERS who pressed for Jesus' arrest, Pilate represented the Roman government. As the governor of the province of Judea, he had the authority to condemn a person to crucifixion. The death sentence was the only outcome the Jewish leaders who opposed Jesus would accept, and they incited a crowd to press Pilate for this decision by claiming that Jesus was a threat to Caesar.

The Jewish leaders were no friends of the Romans under ordinary circumstances. That they would press Pilate on the issue of Jesus tells us how much they hated Jesus and his message.

During the annual festival, the governor could release a prisoner from a "death row" sentence. Pilate did not see that what Jesus had done was especially harmful. Who was he hurting? Certainly not Caesar. So he suggested that Jesus should be released as this year's pardon. But the crowd shouted for the release of Barabbas—a known criminal and murderer.

Pilate was unconvinced of Jesus' guilt and literally washed his hands of the matter after giving the people what they wanted. This was another step in the injustice that happened to Jesus—because Pilate was willing to turn his head away from what he either did not care about or couldn't be bothered with. There's a lesson for all of us in his action. What are we too quick to turn away from when our action could bring a different result for someone's suffering?

HEALTH TIP

Diabetes is the seventh leading cause of death in the United States. Symptoms of diabetes include frequent urination, excessive thirst, unexplained weight loss, extreme hunger, sudden vision changes, tingling or numbness in hands or feet, fatigue, dry skin, sores that are slow to heal, and more infections than usual. A simple blood test can determine if you have diabetes or prediabetes, and you can learn to take good care of yourself with this disease.

— DAILY HEALTH JOURNAL —

Number of steps ....   ◯ Add 3 servings of vegetables
◯ Add 2,000 steps   ◯ Add 3 glasses of water

To Golgotha

MARK 15:20-26

*And they crucified him, and divided his clothes among them,
casting lots to decide what each should take.*
—Mark 15:24

SIMON OF CYRENE PROBABLY had made the pilgrimage from North Africa to celebrate Passover in Jerusalem. After being flogged and publicly shamed, individuals condemned to crucifixion were expected—somehow—to carry their own crosses through the streets. When Jesus stumbled with the effort, Simon was recruited—not in a way he could have declined—to take the load from Jesus onto his own shoulders.

Although Jesus predicted his death to his disciples, in the end they were not prepared for the swiftness of events. On the path to Golgotha, Jesus was subjected to mockery and taunting repeatedly. If any of his disciples were watching from the edges of the crowd, they would have seen the inhumane jest in the sign over Jesus' head. This sign ought to have spelled out his crime. But Jesus was never found guilty of a crime within the Roman system, so the best that could go on the sign was "King of the Jews," a reminder of the blasphemy Jewish leaders accused him of.

Roman soldiers had the right to take for themselves whatever clothing the criminals wore to their execution sites. While they waited for Jesus to die, the Roman guards amused themselves by gambling for his clothing. In their eyes, this is what his life was reduced to—nothing of meaning. Pausing in our own spiritual journeys to remember the humiliation Jesus was subjected to reminds us that Jesus knows our suffering because of what he himself suffered.

HEALTH TIP

Human tears contain substances to bathe the eye, prevent infections, and keep membranes moist. Healthy, cleaner eyes can lead to better vision. Many of us are more prone to tears in times of stress, and these tears help rid the body of chemicals that raise levels of stress hormones, allowing us also to release the sensation of being physically pent-up. Tears can also show what words cannot, becoming a way of communicating more transparently to improve relationships.

— DAILY HEALTH JOURNAL —

Number of steps ....

○ Add 2,000 steps

○ Add 3 servings of vegetables

○ Add 3 glasses of water

On the Cross

MARK 15:33-37

Then Jesus gave a loud cry and breathed his last.
—Mark 15:37

MARK TELLS US THAT DARKNESS fell over the land at noon on that Friday until Jesus died at three in the afternoon. The wine vinegar offered to Jesus in a belated gesture of recognizing his physical agony was a sour wine, a drink of common laborers.

Ordinarily death by crucifixion was a drawn out event. Those crucified suffered for long periods, trying to hold themselves up enough to take one more breath as they became more and more weak and exhausted. If it was taking too long for the convenience of the Roman guard, soldiers might break the legs of the crucified to hasten the process of making them sag between outstretched arms, falling into unconsciousness and no longer able to fill their lungs.

What Mark describes is not this usual death by crucifixion, where victims died slowly and might have hung on the cross for a period of time before anyone noticed or cared that they had died. Jesus gave a loud cry—something that would have taken an intentional effort and deep breath. Right up until the very end of his life, Jesus was the master of the situation, dying not in failure but in fulfillment of a life given to bring the kingdom of God near. Even when we find ourselves in times of deep illness, where cure may not be possible, God may yet have a purpose that our lives will fulfill.

HEALTH TIP

A stroke happens when a blood vessel carrying oxygen to the brain becomes blocked by a clot or bursts. Then part of the brain cannot get the blood and oxygen it needs and begins to die. Signs that a stroke may be occurring include sudden numbness or weakness of the face, arm or leg, sudden confusion, trouble speaking, seeing double, dizziness, loss of coordination, and sudden severe headache. Every second counts in getting help.

--- **DAILY HEALTH JOURNAL** ---

Number of steps ....   ○ Add 3 servings of vegetables
○ Add 2,000 steps   ○ Add 3 glasses of water

At the Foot of the Cross

MARK 15:38-41

Now when the centurion, who stood facing him, saw that in this way he breathed his last, he said, "Truly this man was God's Son!"
—Mark 15:39

ONE ROMAN SOLDIER STOOD out from those who were casting lots of Jesus' clothing. A centurion was a career soldier who worked his way up through the ranks to a position of commanding 100 foot soldiers. The officer on duty at the foot of the cross likely had seen enough crucifixions to know the signs of impending death—though the darkness that covered the land the day Jesus was crucified certainly would have caught the attention of everyone watching that day.

The centurion was attentive, facing Jesus as he took his last breath. In many ways this death was the gory anguish of the execution style the Romans practiced. But between the midday darkness and the effort of a loud cry that a person in the throes of crucifixion should not have been capable of, the centurion knew this was not a typical execution.

"Truly this man was God's Son!" would not have been a widespread acknowledgment to come out of the mouth of a Roman soldier. In this moment the centurion glimpsed the divine purpose.

Often suffering obscures our vision of God's divine work in our lives, and the ways we suffer manifest in our health. The suffering may be an extreme illness or a chronic one. Illness may result from stress that builds up because of other kinds of suffering. The centurion, whom we might least expect to notice the work of God's kingdom, reminds us to expect God to work even in our most strenuous experiences.

HEALTH TIP

The eyes that allow us to see the world are also sometimes described as the "window to the soul." Keeping eyes physically healthy is an important aspect of overall well-being. Undiagnosed diseases such as high blood pressure and diabetes can lead to loss of eyesight. Investigate any changes in vision to rule out the possibility that they are related to disease or to get early treatment if they are.

— DAILY HEALTH JOURNAL —

Number of steps.............................
○ Add 2,000 steps

○ Add 3 servings of vegetables
○ Add 3 glasses of water

At the Tomb

MARK 15:42-47

Then Joseph bought a linen cloth, and taking down the body, wrapped it in the linen cloth, and laid it in a tomb that had been hewn out of the rock.
—Mark 15:46

TIME WAS OF THE ESSENCE, at least to observant Jews. Joseph of Arimathea was a member of the Sanhedrin, but despite the opposition of his colleagues, he believed the kingdom of God had come in Jesus.

However, it was Friday afternoon—past three o'clock already. At sunset, the Jewish Sabbath would begin. Work of any kind would cease, including a suitable burial. Joseph went to Pilate—"boldly," Mark says—and asked for the body of Jesus. After the Sabbath, there would be time to more fully prepare the body with the spices that were among the burial customs. In the meantime, Joseph risked his own reputation to do what he could before sunset.

Joseph wrapped Jesus' body in a cloth purchased at his own expense, laid it in the tomb, and made sure that a heavy stone was rolled into place to secure the burial site until Sunday morning. The watching women, with no real social standing, could do even less for Jesus, but they made sure they knew where the body was laid.

What a helpless evening that must have been for all of them! Their desire to properly prepare Jesus' body points us to the importance of our own grieving rituals. When grief is deepest we share our feelings with those who share our love for the person we've lost. Grief is not something to avoid or rush but to walk through for as long as it takes to find healing.

HEALTH TIP

Spices, used in food as well as burials, add flavor to food but few calories. Seasoning with herbs and spices decreases the amount of salt, fat, and sugar without skimping on flavor. Tastier foods better satisfy the appetite than bland food. Meals that don't satisfy the taste buds increase the likelihood of overeating and compromise efforts to maintain a healthy weight. Gradually try out new seasonings until you find your new favorite.

— DAILY HEALTH JOURNAL —

Number of steps.............................   O Add 3 servings of vegetables
O Add 2,000 steps   O Add 3 glasses of water

The Empty Tomb
MARK 16:1–8

*And very early on the first day of the week, when
the sun had risen, they went to the tomb.*
—Mark 16:2

WHEN THE WOMEN LEFT their homes that Sunday morning, ready with their spices, anxiety compounded their grief at losing Jesus. Even together, they would not be able to move the stone Joseph of Arimathea had used to seal the tomb.

We know the resurrection story well enough to know that the open—and empty—tomb meant Jesus had risen from the dead, but the women did not know that. Their shock would have been full of questions. Where was Jesus' body? Why would someone take it?

Even when they saw the angel we have come to expect in the story, they were alarmed. Imagine their minds trying to make sense of the unbelievable words he spoke.

The women who on Friday night could do nothing for Jesus were now entrusted with being the first messengers of the good news. "Go," the angel said, "tell his disciples." The angel made special mention of Peter. Despite his very public failing, Jesus had work for Peter to do. Peter would still be part of the group who would carry on the work Jesus had prepared them for.

In our Easter traditions, we might hear trumpets and organs and choirs or worship bands prepared with triumphant music. After we have lived through the tension of Holy Week and the darkness of Good Friday, we rejoice in the brightness of God's healing work not only in our own lives but in the history of the world.

HEALTH TIP

We often associate Easter with the season of spring and signs of new life in nature. What about signs of new life in you? Are you refreshing your body with rest and nutrition? Are you renewing habits of health and hope? Are you reviving your faith experience through Bible reading and the sacraments? These are all ways of going deeper into understanding what health and wholeness mean for our lives.

— **DAILY HEALTH JOURNAL** —

Number of steps _____   ○ Add 3 servings of vegetables
○ Add 2,000 steps   ○ Add 3 glasses of water

Week Six in Review

THE PAST WEEK OF meditations led us through the crucifixion and resurrection of Jesus and, for us in this program, marks the beginning of a new life filled with good health, activity, and a revitalized spirit.

You have come to an end point in six weeks of *Walking with Jesus*, but you are also beginning anew. This program was designed to help you establish some healthy lifestyle changes that you will carry on through your years. Reflect on the ways you have succeeded in your journey, what you have discovered about yourself along the way, and what you'd like to set your sights on next.

Transfer your daily steps in the space below. If you set a goal for all three categories, put checkmarks in the boxes where you reached your goal for each day.

Number of steps	Add 2,000 steps	Add 3 vegetables	Add 3 glasses of water
Day 1	○	○	○
Day 2	○	○	○
Day 3	○	○	○
Day 4	○	○	○
Day 5	○	○	○
Day 6	○	○	○
Day 7	○	○	○

— Congratulations! —

YOU HAVE COMPLETED *Walking with Jesus.* By increasing your steps, adding 3 servings of vegetables, and adding 3 glasses of water each day, you have taken some steps in the right direction.

It's important to continue the lifestyle changes you've made during the last six weeks. Treat yourself to a new pair of walking shoes. Explore a museum, zoo, or nature preserve. You may even consider walking in a charity 5K with a friend. Think of fun ways to reward yourself that will relate to your new lifestyle and motivate you to continue your new habits.

Please take a few minutes to answer the following questions and return the completed form to your project coordinator.

Name: ....

Congregation or Community Organization: ....

....

1. I was able to add 2,000 steps to my daily activity.
   ○ Never   ○ Seldom   ○ Sometimes   ○ Often   ○ Always

2. I was able to add 3 servings of vegetables to my daily meals.
   ○ Never   ○ Seldom   ○ Sometimes   ○ Often   ○ Always

3. I was able to add 3 glasses of water to my fluid fluids.
   ○ Never   ○ Seldom   ○ Sometimes   ○ Often   ○ Always

4. I found *Walking with Jesus* to be helpful and it inspired me to reach my goals.
   ○ Never   ○ Seldom   ○ Sometimes   ○ Often   ○ Always

5. How many days a week do you engage in some type of mild to moderate physical activity (walking slowly, gardening, housework, window shopping, and so on)?   Days per week ....

6. How many days a week do you engage in some type of moderate to vigorous physical activity (brisk walking, running, riding a bike, dancing, playing a sport and so on)?   **Days per week** ....

CUT HERE ✂

7. Which answer best describes how you feel about the following?

	I have no plans to	I plan to in the future	I plan to immediately	I have been doing so for *fewer* than six months	I have been doing so for *more* than six months
Increasing physical activity					
Improving nutrition					

8. To what degree do you feel that your physical health and spiritual health are connected?

○ Not at all   ○ Quite a bit
○ A little bit   ○ Extremely
○ Moderately

9. What comments would you like to share with the project coordinator?

Thank you for participating! Please return this form to the project coordinator in your congregation or community organization.

CUT HERE

CONTINUE THE JOURNEY TO HEALTH

More from the Ways to Wellness series ...

Work on health goals for six weeks
while meditating on Scripture readings
that follow the walking routes of
ABRAHAM & SARAH and **PAUL.**

About the Author

SUSAN MARTINS MILLER has been a writer and editor for over 30 years, creating faith-based resources for children and adults to use both at home and in congregational settings. She holds a master's degree in biblical studies (New Testament) from Trinity Evangelical Divinity School.

Walking with Jesus is part of the Ways to Wellness series, which also includes *Walking with Abraham and Sarah* and *Walking with Paul*.

CPSIA information can be obtained
at www.ICGtesting.com
Printed in the USA
LVHW111435010321
680270LV00027B/212